Together, Even When We're Apart

My Neighborhood's Stories of the COVID-19 Pandemic

Published in the United States by One Heart Books
All rights reserved.

Library of Congress Control Number: 2020924860

Paperback ISBN 978-1-7362220-0-3
Ebook ISBN 978-1-7362220-1-0
Hardcover ISBN 978-1-7362220-2-7

Illustrations and book design by Anna Myers

For the most up-to-date information about COVID-19,
please visit the World Health Organization's website at
www.who.int/emergencies/diseases/novel-coronavirus-2019

Learn more about One Heart Books: www.facebook.com/oneheartbooks

Also coming soon from One Heart Books:
A Sunday Night in September: A Story about Dizzy Gillespie and Enoch Olinga

Together, Even When We're Apart

My Neighborhood's Stories of the COVID-19 Pandemic

By Linda Ahdieh Grant

Illustrated by Anna Myers

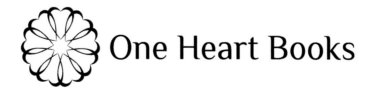 One Heart Books

REGO PARK, NEW YORK
DECATUR, GEORGIA
USA

A Note to Parents, Caregivers, and Educators

At dinner tables around the world, families are talking about coronavirus and how to keep everyone safe. Because it is a new virus, no one's body has a memory of it and it can infect anyone. Not everyone gets infected, but some people become very sick when they are infected and can even die. This is a time of confusion and uncertainty, and also of fellow feeling and common endeavor.

This book was written for small children who are experiencing the coronavirus pandemic. Our hope is that it will be a source of knowledge and insights, and a reminder that all human beings – no matter who they are – are capable of being deeply concerned with the well-being of others, and also that every community – wherever it may be – is capable of tremendous solidarity.

We hope that every child who reads this book will feel assured that this challenging period will eventually pass and that when it is over we will have a much better understanding of our interdependence and inherent oneness.

In the meantime, each of us - even our community's youngest members – can be a candle in the darkness and a champion of unity, not only in the future when they grow up, but also right now as a child in 2020.

Together, Even When We're Apart

My Neighborhood's Stories of the COVID-19 Pandemic

By Linda
Ahdieh Grant

Illustrated by
Anna Myers

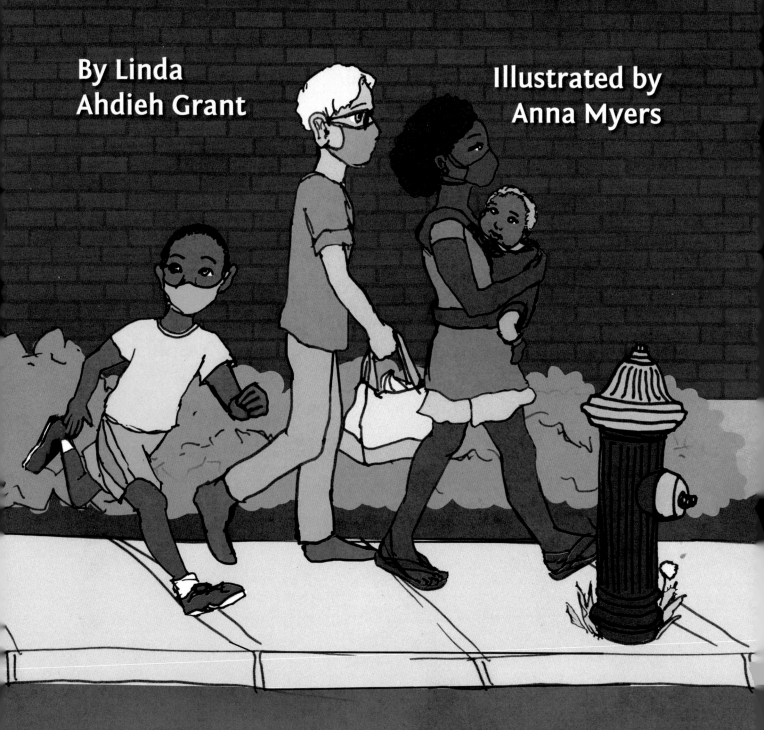

THE McCALLISTER

is a red brick building
   on the corner of Central Avenue and 62nd Street.
It was built long ago
even before my parents were born.
It takes us 5 minutes to walk to the bus stop
   and two blocks to walk to the playground.
It is also my home,
   and the home of my neighbors.
Let me tell you a little bit more about the McCallister
and the people who live there.

MY NAME IS AMARI

I'm 7, and I live with my mom, my dad,
   and my new baby sister.
I used to go to school, and play with my friends at the park,
but then people all over the world got really sick
with COVID-19, or coronavirus.

Now, my family and neighbors are keeping each other safe.
By staying inside.
By washing our hands.
By wearing a mask.
By coughing and sneezing into a tissue.
By not touching our face.
By going to school in new ways.

Sometimes I feel lonely and bored,
but I remember to be grateful for what I have,
and to keep myself and others safe
and teach my baby sister something new
and look for something helpful to do around the house.

KIMMY AND HER BROTHER KENDRICK

live with their aunt and uncle
in the apartment above me.
They used to go to work early and come home late.
Kimmy worked at the airport and brought me
cinnamon gum.
Kendrick worked at the movies and told me which ones
were coming up.
I used to hear their footsteps early in the morning and
late at night,
but now I don't
because they lost their jobs.
This is a big problem because they help pay the rent.
Last night I made them mac and cheese and left it
outside their door.
I wish I could do more.
I wish
their footsteps would wake me up again
so they would be back at work.

Those are the words that describe her face.
Every day she takes care of patients who are very sick.
And every day, she puts the lives of others
before her own.
Every night at 7 o'clock we open our windows and
   clap and cheer for her
   and everyone working in hospitals who
   are called the First Responders.
People in their cars blow their
horns to say thank you.
On my first day of learning at home,
she put a note with her phone number on everyone's door.
She told us to call her if we have any questions.
It makes me feel safe and also proud
   that she lives in my building.

MRS. ANITA AND MY MASK

My mom told me that we must wear a mask
 when we go outside,
  because the coronavirus could go from one person
  to another person even if no one seems sick.
The mask is like a shield
 for other people in case I am sick, and also
 for me in case other people are sick.
One day there was a note under our door.
Our neighbor Mrs. Anita was making masks
 for everyone in the building,
 even me.
She asked if I had a favorite color.
And I wrote her back,
"Yes! Green, please."
Now I have a mask, and
 I feel like a hero,
  protecting everyone with my shield.

LILLY AND LUKE

are my friends and are twins.
During these days that we are all inside
   and because they only have each other to play with
   and because their parents are working from home,
   Lilly and Luke made a goal to help each other get
   better at sports.
They have a few little balls and decided
   to try to juggle more and more balls
   for a longer and longer time.
Before the pandemic, they could juggle only 1 ball
   for about 5 minutes before they dropped it.
Now they can keep 3 balls in the air for 8 minutes.
I wonder how much better they will get by the time the
   pandemic ends.
I can't wait for them to teach me, too.

MRS. C

lives down the hall.

She has a cat named Gerkin.

Dad sometimes brings her groceries

And she likes to treat us to beignets.

But then Mrs. C got very sick with coronavirus.

Paramedics took her to the hospital.

She had to stay there for a long time so
  the doctors could help her get better.

Gerkin has been living down the hall with Mr. Gonzalo
  and will be happy to see Mrs. C when she comes home
  next week.

So will I.

We are going to put balloons outside of her door so she
  knows we are happy she is back.

I have been practicing her famous beignet recipe,
  and I can't wait to make her some.

MR. GONZALO

lives all alone on the first floor.

Before the virus, his family would come to visit him.

But now they can't because they are sheltering in place,
   or staying at home.

Because he is older, and has diabetes, he could get very sick
   if he catches the virus from a hug or a kiss, or even
   droplets in the air.

Our family has adopted him as our "bonus" grandpa and
   we call him every single day
   with a funny joke or riddle to tell him.

I think this makes him feel happy and less alone.

I never noticed him as much before,
   but somehow now I am always thinking of ways to make
   him laugh.

Even if this virus is keeping
   us apart,
   at the same time it has
   brought us
   closer together.

I wonder if someone is telling jokes to my grandpa, too.

LI-SU

is my next door neighbor
She is five and we go to the same school.
She misses her teacher and her classmates.
Her mom reminds her to be hopeful and that it is OK to be
   scared,
   or sad,
   or angry,
   or confused.
She reminds Li-Su to mix those feelings with thankfulness.
Her teacher told her mom to practice reading with her
   every day.
She is getting better at it.

Her mom says it is like jumping rope.
   You need to practice even when it's hard.
   And then all of a sudden it is easy.
To make reading more fun, her mom asked me to help.
Li-Su calls me every day at 1:00 and we read to
   each other.
For me, it is my favorite part of the day.

MARIO'S DAD

Mario lives on the 3rd floor and is my best friend.

Mario's dad has worked every day
  since the pandemic began.

His grocery shop does things to keep people healthy.
  They have special hours for people more than 60.
  You have to wear a mask, and there
  is hand sanitizer at the door.
  Only 5 people can be inside at a time.

Even though his family is worried he may get sick,
he asks "What will people eat if I close?"

The other day, he brought each person in our building
a
bar
of soap.
My friend Mario put happy face stickers on each one.
His dad sent us a text reminding us
to wash our hands with a lot of
soap for at least 20 seconds.
Because soap and water
kill the virus.

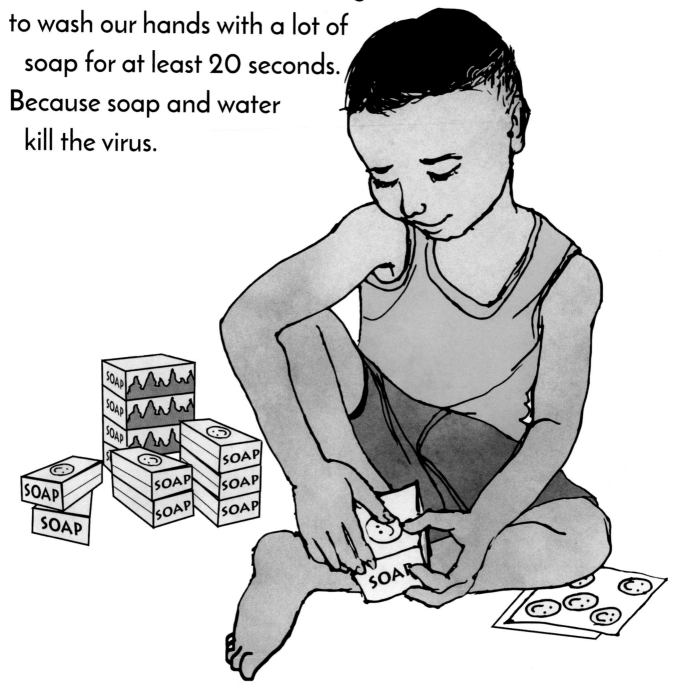

He gave us soap so we don't skip
washing our hands
if we run out.
He also told us to sing the happy
birthday song twice because that
takes 20 seconds to sing.
I sing happy birthday in my head to
Mario's dad every time
I wash my hands
because
I am happy
he was born.

MISS Z

is my favorite grownup
   on our floor.
Before the pandemic, she used to
   play hopscotch with us
   outside the building door.
She is a teacher and very funny.
She teaches her 4th grade class
   on the computer now.
She has also become an
   adopted teacher for the kids in
   the McCallister.
When we heard on the news to
   practice social distancing
   and stand 6 feet apart from
   everyone, she knew that some of
   us didn't know what that meant.
So, she cut pieces of yarn 6 feet long
and gave one to each child in the building.
Because when you are small like me 6 feet feels very, very far.
Maybe she'll teach us about fractions next.
   I hope so.

DR. TENEA

moved into our building when there was snow on the
  ground.
With all the places to live, I am glad the McCalister is
  what she found.
She is helping to make a vaccine to stop COVID-19,
  so that it will not be so dangerous.
I never thought I would be happy to get a shot,
  but my parents tell me that it will help a lot.
Kind and smart scientists are working hard to find
  a way.
I say prayers and send good wishes to them every day.
Dr. Tenea is part of this global team.
She works hard
    even on Saturdays and Sundays.
On Friday nights, my dad and I make popcorn for her
    to eat while she watches movies.
I wonder if my popcorn is helping somehow?
I wonder if I can learn enough in school to make a
  vaccine one day?

STAYING HEALTHY

My mom told me that
  I should
  try and stay healthy.
Wash my hands with soap.
Sleep enough. Eat well. Exercise every day. Be happy.
My mom loves to cook and she sometimes makes my
  favorites for dinner.
And sometimes my not so favorites.
Like beans and rice. But that's OK.
My dad goes to the market to buy food
  and sometimes we get a special
  delivery of vegetables
  from Ms. Park's garden.

MS. PARK

Last year, when I was 6, I helped Ms. Park plant vegetables.

We named the plants and wrote their
   names on popsicle sticks.

I miss that day so, so much.

This year, I couldn't help, but Ms. Park sends me pictures
   every Monday so I can watch the seeds grow.

The plants have grown a lot and she
   brings us some of the harvest.

   Yummy basil to put on our pasta.

   Mint that my dad drinks in his tea.

   Small tomatoes that my mom cooks and that
   I don't like so much.

Even then, it makes me happy to grow food.

I am glad that Ms. Park doesn't keep it all for herself
   and shares with me and her neighbors.

NEIGHBORS

Every Friday night after I brush my teeth,

I run to the couch to join my family on a computer call

with all of my neighbors for a devotional meeting

that I have nicknamed "McCallister Meets."

For 30 minutes, we say prayers and tell stories.

It was started by my neighbor Ruth and me

because she wanted to say prayers with me and the people

she loves

and make sure everyone is doing OK.

Even though people in my building are from different faiths

and religions, we all believe in being good people

and we are united in our love for each other.

And even though our bodies are not together,
  our hearts and minds are closer than before.
There are some neighbors that I didn't even know before
  and now
  we are friends.
We talk about how everyone is doing.
We have found lots of ways to help each other.
During these calls, I forget for a while that we are in
  different rooms
  and feel like
  everyone in the building is hugging me tight.

During these days when time is standing still
and we may sometimes feel sad or
confused or tired of being inside,
we can remember, that all of us –
my family, my neighbors, and me –
are still together, we still need each
other, and we will get through this.
Together.
And at the other end, we will be
stronger, much stronger.
My mom told me human beings
are meant to cooperate with
each other.
Like notes in my piano songs,
like rivers, streams, and drops that
come together to make the sea.
She told me that
the whole world will be strong
if we learn to show with our actions
that we are united.
I think my neighbors are doing that,
and hopefully I am too.

What is happening in your building and your neighborhood?
Who is helping you? Who are you helping?

Here in my apartment building, we are together even
though we are apart.
Cooperation and love have brought us together like
never before,
and if we all try really hard,
then maybe the same thing will happen in every place
on earth.

"So powerful is the light of unity that it can
illuminate the whole earth." — *Bahá'í Writings*

QUESTIONS TO EXPLORE

What is happening in your home/building
and your neighborhood?

Who is helping you?

Who are you helping?

Draw a picture of people that are important to you in your community

Dedicated to the Children of the World

Linda Ahdieh Grant has a BA in Anthropology from Haverford College and a PhD in Epidemiology from Johns Hopkins School of Public Health. Writing this story with Anna combined some of her favorite things — the spirit of children, science, and the power of community. She lives in Decatur, Georgia with her family.

Anna Myers has a BA in Drawing, Painting, and Printmaking from Bard College at Simon's Rock, and an MFA in Illustration from Western Connecticut State University. In her work she hopes to show the children who read her books that love for humanity can heal the world. She lives in Queens, New York with her family.

Special thanks to....

Bahiyyih, Erica, Farnoosh, Frank III and Frank IV, Gavin, Homa, Hussein, Jane, Joann, Johanna, Laurie, Marc, Missy, Richard, Robert, Shannon, Tahereh, Tatiana, Terra, Thomas, and Viola

Made in the USA
Columbia, SC
01 February 2021

32172957R00024